Chester Music for Viola

arranged and edited by

Watson Forbes

Chester Music

(A Division of Music Sales Limited)
8/9 Frith Street, London, W1D 3JB
Exclusive Distributors: Music Sales Ltd., Newmarket Road,
Bury St. Edmund, Suffolk, IP33 3YB

for Jean

BERCEUSE

Arranged for Violin (or Viola) and Piano by
WATSON FORBES

ALEXANDER ILYINSKY
(1859-1919)

Duration:- 2 minutes

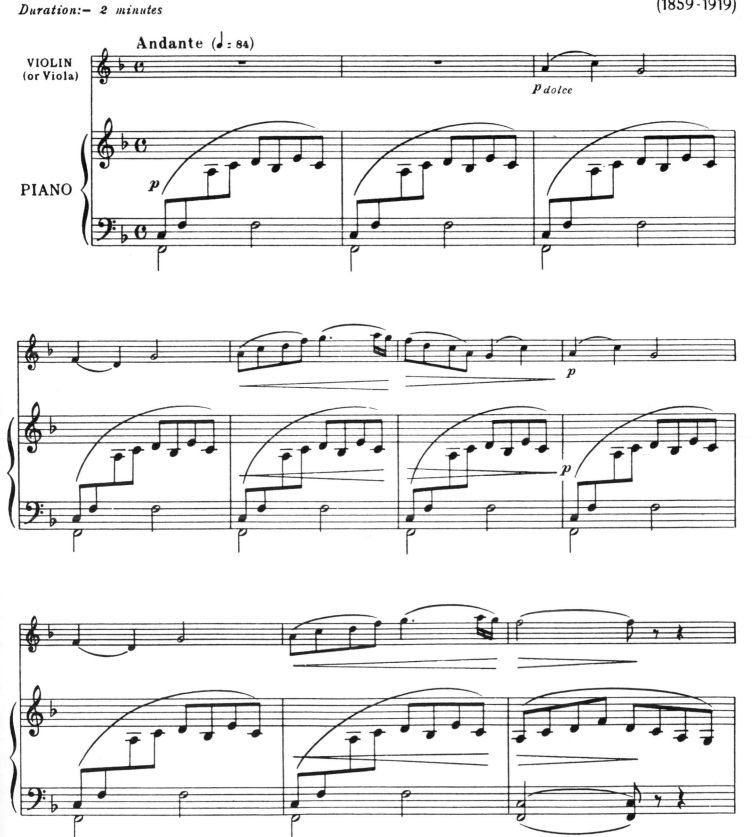

BOURRÉE AND HORNPIPE

6

Duration 1¾ minutes

Arranged for Viola and Piano by
WATSON FORBES

BOURRÉE

HENRY PURCELL
(1658-1695)

attacca Hornpipe

HORNPIPE

D.C. Bourrée al Fine.

for Jean

BERCEUSE AND DANCE

Arranged for Viola and Piano by
WATSON FORBES

VLADIMIR REBIKOFF
(1866 -1920)

Duration :- *1½ minutes*

1. BERCEUSE

for Jean

2. DANCE

Duration:- 1½ minutes

Arranged for Viola and Piano by
WATSON FORBES

VLADIMIR REBIKOFF
(1866-1920)

for Jean

BARCAROLLE

Arranged for Violin (or Viola) and Piano by
WATSON FORBES

Duration:– 4 minutes

TCHAIKOWSKY
Op. 37ª No. 6.

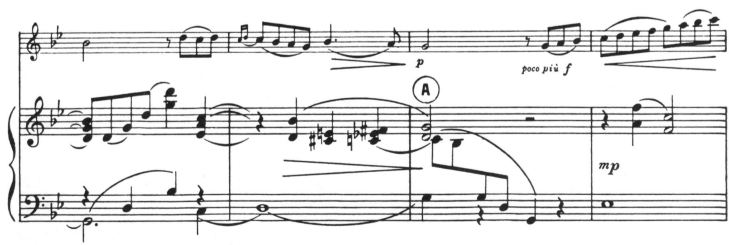

Poco più mosso

Poco più mosso

for Jean

CHANSON TRISTE

Arranged for Viola and Piano by
WATSON FORBES

Duration:– 3 minutes

TCHAIKOWSKY
Op. 40. No. 2.

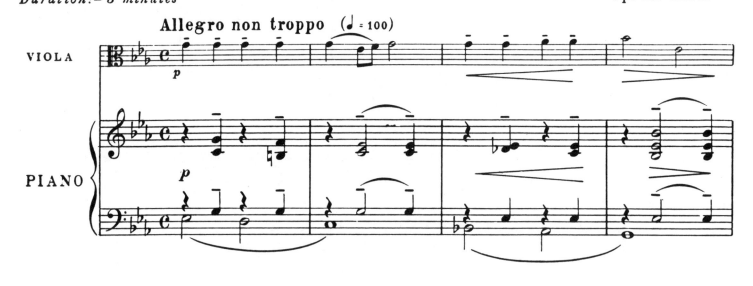

May be played entirely in the first position or with simple changes between the first three positions.

for Jean

CHANSON ITALIENNE

Arranged for Viola and Piano by
WATSON FORBES

Duration:- 1¼ minutes

TCHAIKOWSKY
Op. 39. No. 15.

May be played entirely in the first position. The fingering gives
some suggestions for simple changes between the first three positions.

SONG WITHOUT WORDS

Op. 19. Nº 1

Duration: 3 mins.

Arranged for Viola and Piano by
WATSON FORBES

MENDELSSOHN

* This repeat should always be made since the Viola part is written out and is played one octave lower the second time through

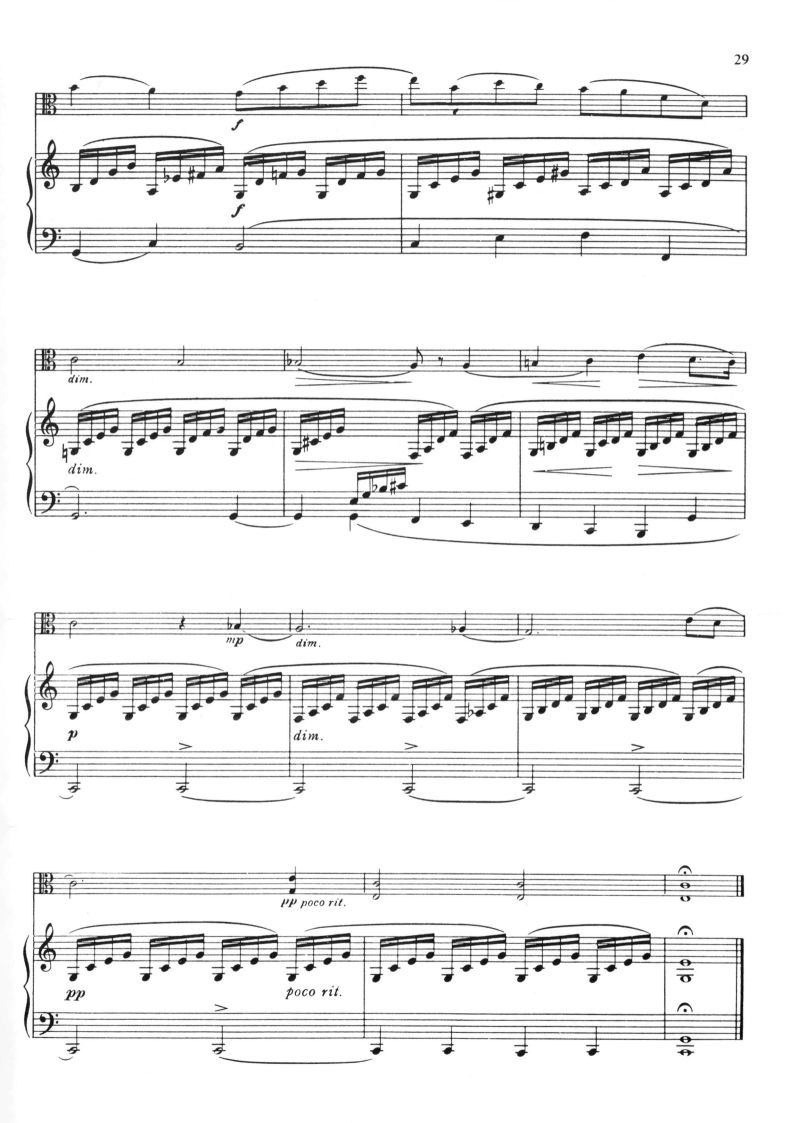

SONG WITHOUT WORDS

Op. 38. No 2

Duration: 2½ mins.

Arranged for Viola and Piano by
WATSON FORBES

MENDELSSOHN